# MIND GAMES

Sarah Blackmore

Published in association with The Basic Skills Agency

Hodder & Stoughton

A MEMBER OF THE HODDER HEADLINE GROUP

**Acknowledgements**

Cover: Oscar Burriel/Science Photo Library

Photos: pp 3, 5, 8. 10, 17 Mary Evans Photo Library; p 14 BSIP Boucharlat/Science Photo Library; pp 21, 25 Hulton Getty

Every effort has been made to trace copyright holders of material reproduced in this book. Any rights not acknowledged will be acknowledged in subsequent printings if notice is given to the publisher.

Orders; please contact Bookpoint Ltd, 39 Milton Park, Abingdon, Oxon OX14 4TD. Telephone: (44) 01235 400414, Fax: (44) 01235 400454. Lines are open from 9.00–6.00, Monday to Saturday, with a 24 hour message answering service.
Email address: orders@bookpoint.co.uk

*British Library Cataloguing in Publication Data*
A catalogue record for this title is available from the British Library

ISBN 0 340 77647 1

First published 2000
Impression number 10 9 8 7 6 5 4 3 2 1
Year 2005 2004 2003 2002 2001 2000



Adapted for the Livewire series by Sarah Blackmore



Typeset by GreenGate Publishing Services, Tonbridge, Kent.
Printed in Great Britain for Hodder and Stoughton Educational, a division of Hodder Headline Plc, 338 Euston Road, London NW1 3BH, by Redwood Books, Trowbridge, Wilts

# Contents

# 1 You Feel Sleepy …

'You feel sleepy.
Your eyes are getting heavy.
Watch the light …'

The voice goes on and on and on …

'You are getting sleepy, very sleepy.'

Have you heard that sentence before?
Maybe you have seen hypnotists on TV.
Sometimes they use that sentence to hypnotise people.

The cover of a popular French manual in the early 1900s.

# 2 What is Hypnosis?

For a long time it was thought to be a trick.
A kind of party game.
Only a few people believed in it.
They thought it could be used to heal the sick.
Most doctors laughed at this.
They did not believe in party tricks.
They did not believe in mind games.

Things are different now.
A lot of people believe in hypnosis.
A lot of people believe that it has many uses.

Charcot demonstrating the symptoms of hysteria with a patient under hypnosis (1887).

So what is hypnosis?
What happens when you are hypnotised?
Some people think that
one part of the brain shuts down.
Others say that the body is really relaxed
but the mind stays open.

One doctor describes hypnosis in this way:

'It is like going to the cinema.
When you go in you see everything.
You hear the sound of sweet papers,
people coughing and talking.
You see the head of the person in front of you.

When the film starts things change.
You become really interested in the film,
and don't notice the other things.

That's how it is with hypnosis.
Your mind is set on one thing.
You don't notice other things.'

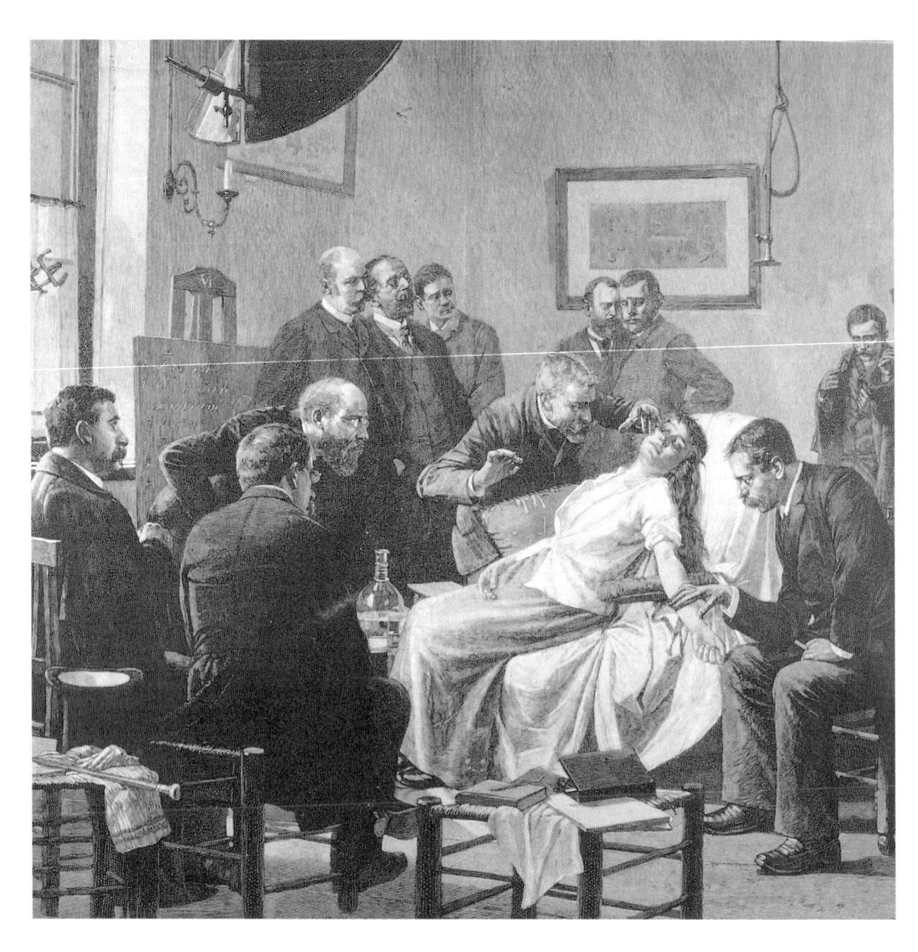

German doctors observe a demonstration of hypnotism in 1893.

# 3 Does it Work?

Most people don't want to know what hypnosis is.
They do want to know if it really works.

Will it work on me?
Will it help me to stop smoking?
Will it help me to lose weight?
Will it help me to stop being afraid of heights?
Will it help me to stop being afraid of flying?

People want to know other things.
Will it help to take away pain?
Will it help me to remember things?

Mesmer gives a demonstration at his home in Paris (1784).

There is some proof that hypnosis can work.
It has been used to help people stop smoking.

It worked on one smoker.
She had been smoking for 18 years.
Puffing away on two packs of cigarettes a day.
She had tried to give up
but each time she tried to give up, she failed.
In the end she asked to be hypnotised.

It was important that she really wanted to give up.
You have to really want to change.
Only then can hypnosis work.

The smoker was hypnotised.
She was asked to see herself as a non-smoker.
Then she was asked to imagine
that she was in a place where she always smoked.
Under hypnosis she could say,
'No thanks, I don't smoke.'

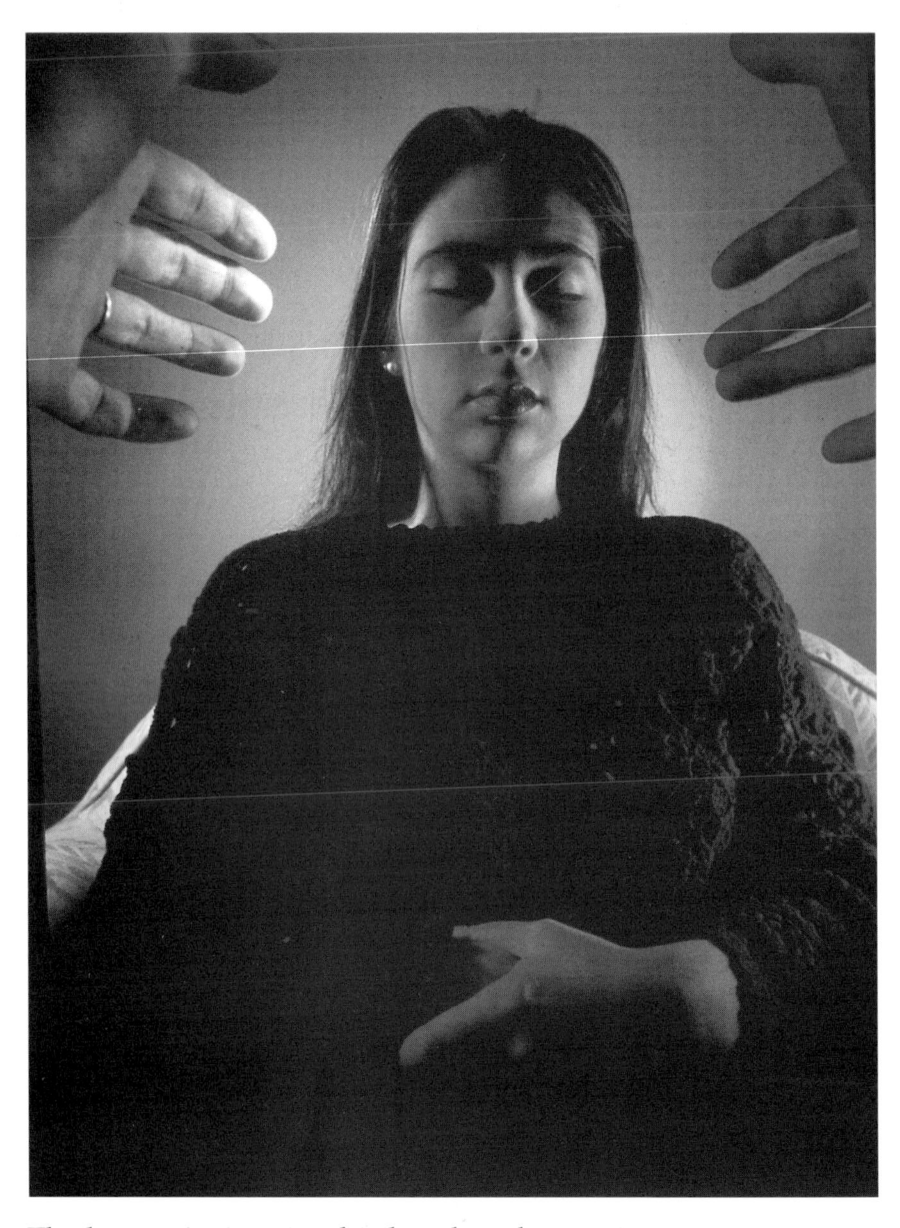

The hypnotist is using his hands to hypnotise a woman.

The hypnosis worked.
She gave up.
She even stopped wanting to smoke.

It is hard to stop smoking.
Hypnosis does not work for everyone.
Only about one smoker in five gives up for good
after hypnosis.

Hypnosis can help
but you have to really want to give up.

# 4 Hypnosis and Pain

What else can hypnosis do?
Can it block pain during an operation?
Most experts think that it can stop some pain.
Some doctors have used it,
and so have some dentists.

Can it block all pain?
There is some proof that it can.

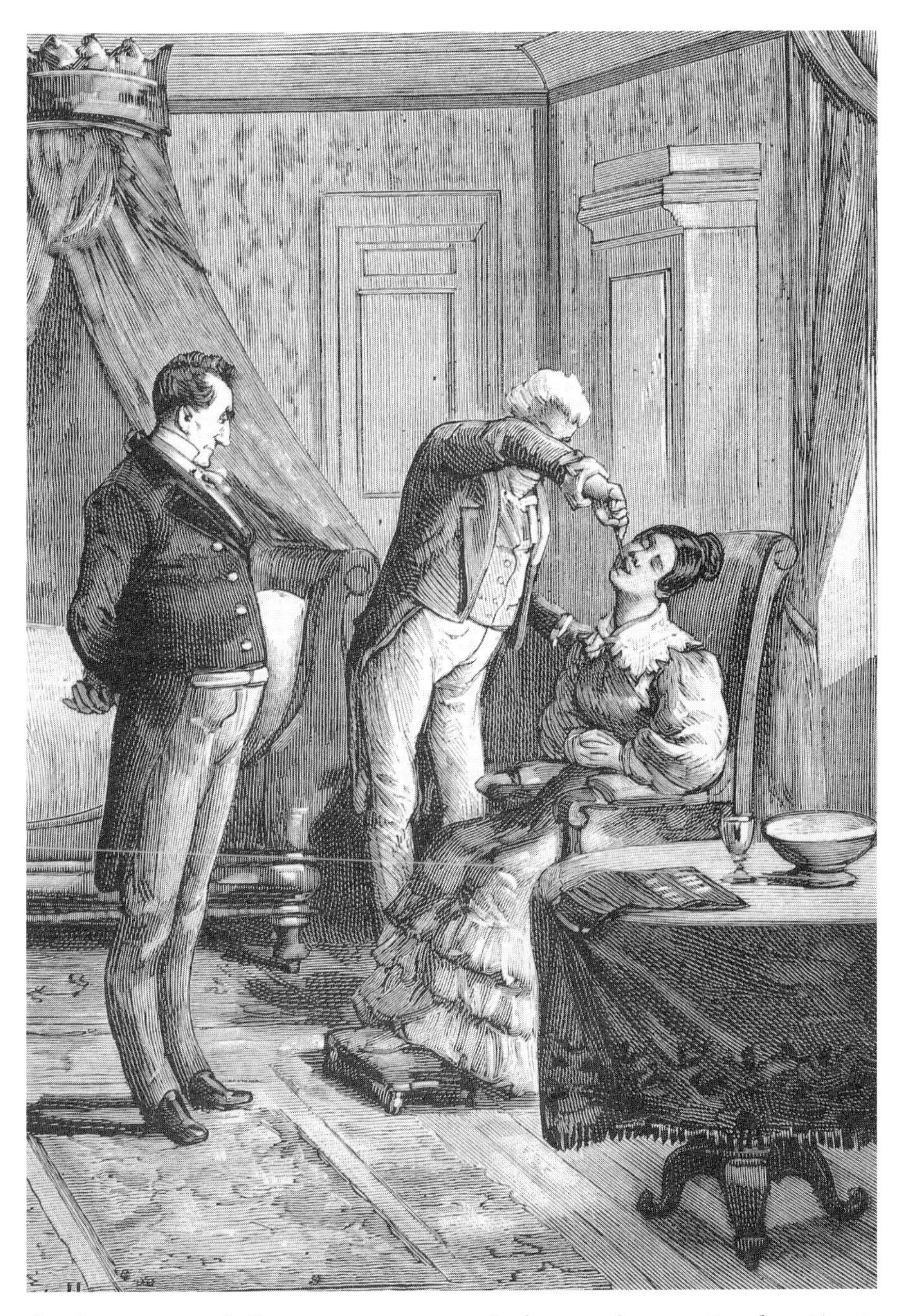

Oudet successfully removes a tooth from a hypnotised patient (14 November 1836).

One man had to have an operation.
Would you want to stay awake during an operation?
Without anything to put you to sleep?
No anaesthetic?

This man wanted to be hypnotised.
Even more, he hypnotised himself.

The man thought about things to relax himself.
He tried to imagine his favourite music,
just before his stomach was cut open.

He was able to talk and joke during the operation.
The operation lasted over an hour.
His pulse rate and blood pressure were fine.
At the end, he got off the table and walked away.

He said that he felt no pain, just a little tug.

# 5 Using Hypnosis in Other Ways

Hypnosis has many uses.
It can help to prevent asthma attacks,
and epileptic fits.
It has also been used to help headaches.

Hypnosis can help to ease pain in many things,
even cancer.

During a 1950s television show, members of the audience were hypnotised to loll in chairs or lie helpless on the stage.

Hypnosis has been used in other ways.
It has been used to help people to remember things.
The police have used it to help solve crimes.

People can remember things when they are hypnotised.
Things that they may not usually remember.
Things that they have blocked out
or are too scared to tell.

People do remember things when they are hypnotised.
However, can we be sure that
they really remember what happens?
People are not really sure.

One American court would not allow a witness
who had been hypnotised.
The court said that it was too difficult to know
if the person was telling the truth.
It was too difficult to work out what was fact
or what was fiction.

# 6 Could you be Hypnotised?

Have you seen a hypnotist on TV?
Or have you seen one in real life?

Did you know that not everybody can be hypnotised?
It is nothing to do with how old you are,
or how clever you are.

You have to want to be hypnotised.

A rigid position can be induced under hypnosis. Here the patient supports Peter Casson's 11½ stone body weight.

If you want to be hypnotised,
you have to have an open mind.
You have to want it to work.
You have to want to concentrate.

Then you will start to feel sleepy.
Very sleepy …

If you have enjoyed reading this book, you may be interested in other titles in the *Livewire* series.

Volcanoes
Custer's Last Stand
Pompeii
The Great Fire of London
The Titanic
The Black Death
Black Holes
The Bermuda Triangle
The Secrets of Vaccination
The Dead Sea Scrolls
UFOs